GW00420384

b

_____

_____

_____

_____

> **Check**
>
> capital letters S + D   exclamation mark !
>
> comma   ,   speech marks " "
>
> full stop   .

Activity 6
Build a sentence

minute _____

_____

_____

_____

Activity 7
Edit

Find 6 errors.

thank you! said Luke to Fran

he stooped to stroke Duke

> **Check**
>
> 2 capital letters   full stops   . .
>
> speech marks   " "

Activity 9
Composition

Power words
minute
freedom

(a) **Write notes about what dogs need.**

Read Write Inc.
PHONICS

Get Writing!

Grey Book 7

Writing activities for Set 7 Grey

Storybooks 1–13 and Non-fiction Books

Name _____

Series developed by **Ruth Miskin**

OXFORD

Rex to the rescue

See *Get Writing!* Handbook for lesson plans.

**Activities
1, 2, 3, 4**
Spelling

Green words

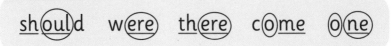

take   while   nose   came   truce

Red words

should   were   there   come   one

Your words

Activity 5
Hold a
sentence

(a)

_____

_____

_____

_____

_____

Check

capital letter W   question mark ?

b Write sentences about what dogs need.

The lion's paw

Green words

found   strange   place   floor   saw

Red words

m@ny   O(ne)   w(ere)   O(th)er   thr(ough)

Your words

ⓐ

Check

capital letter   Y   comma   ,
    full stop   .   speech marks   " "

b

_____

_____

_____

Check

capital letter   Y   comma ,

    full stop   .   speech marks   " "

Activity 6
Build a sentence

horror/horrified _____

_____

_____

Activity 7
Edit

Find 6 errors.

he sor a cave, dug out of the hillside. this looks like a good place to sleep, he said to himself

Check

2 capital letters   1 spell **✗**

    full stop   .   speech marks   " "

Activity 9
Composition

Power words
terror/terrified
horror/horrified
courageous

(a) **Make notes about Androcles.**

• Punishment: _____
_____
_____
_____

• Stepping out into the Arena: _____
_____
_____
_____

• In the Arena: _____
_____
_____
_____

• Safe at last: _____
_____
_____
_____

8

b You are Androcles. Write about what happened to you.

I dare you

Activities 1, 2, 3, 4
Spelling

Green words

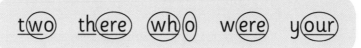

face   stair   hair   care   share

Red words

two   there   who   were   your

Your words

Activity 5
Hold a
sentence

(a)

_____

_____

_____

_____

_____

Check
capital letters W + R + C   question mark ?
apostrophe '

(b)

_____

_____

_____

Check

capital letters W + C   question mark   ?

apostrophe   '

Activity 6
Build a
sentence

crammed _____

_____

_____

_____

Activity 7
Edit

Find 6 errors.

i dar you to put on three pars
of moonboots and climb the
mast, said Clare

Check

1 capital letter   2 spell ✗

full stop •   speech marks " "

11

Activity 9
Composition

Have you ever played Hide and Seek or Sardines? How did you feel?

Power words
cramped
crammed
squeezed

_____

_____

_____

_____

_____

_____

_____

_____

_____

_____

Looking after a hamster

**Activities
1, 2, 3, 4**
Spelling

Green words

f̲i̲rst   li͡ke   ca͡ge   g̲i̲rl   h̲u̲rt

Red words

m⊙th er   ⊙th er   (are)   w⊙nt   y⊙ur

Your words

Activity 5
Hold a
sentence

(a)

_____

_____

_____

_____

_____

Check
capital letter W   question mark ?

b

_____

_____

_____

Check

capital letter W   question mark ?

Activity 6
Build a sentence

clamber _____

_____

_____

_____

_____

Activity 7
Edit

Find 6 errors.

never let an anmal suffu take

it to the vet if it is ill, so that

he or she can make it better

Check

2 capital letters   2 spell ✗

          full stops ..

Power words
scuttle
scurry
clamber
entice

Finish the poem about the hamster
that escaped.

Escaped

We didn't lock the door
We forgot to shut it tight
We should have all made sure
But our pet escaped last night!

_____

_____

_____

_____

_____

_____

_____

_____

_____

How silly!

**Activities
1, 2, 3, 4**
Spelling

Green words

sound   round   brown   town   now

Red words

here   who   there   water   son

Your words

Activity 5
Hold a
sentence

(a)

_____

_____

_____

_____

_____

Check

capital letter   T   exclamation mark   !

full stop   .   speech marks   " "

(b)

_____

_____

_____

Check

capital letter W   question mark   ?

full stop   .   speech marks   " "

Activity 6
Build a sentence

ridiculous _____

_____

_____

_____

Activity 7
Edit

Find 6 errors.

The best grass is on my roof,
he frowned, so i've got to get
the cow up there to eat it

Check

1 capital letter   speech marks " " " "

full stop   .

Activity 9
Composition

(a) **Make notes about when you were embarrassed.**

Power words
ridiculous   nonsense   sensible

b **Now write about what happened.**

When I was embarrassed _____

_____

_____

_____

_____

_____

_____

_____

_____

_____

The most embarrassing moment was _____

_____

_____

_____

_____

Wailing Winny's car boot sale

Activities 1, 2, 3, 4
Spelling

Green words

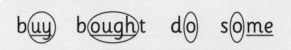

take   face   p<u>ai</u>d   p<u>ai</u>nt   f<u>ai</u>nt

Red words

b⟨uy⟩   b⟨ough⟩t   d⟨o⟩   s⟨o⟩<u>me</u>

Your words

Activity 5
Hold a sentence

(a)

_____

_____

_____

_____

Check

| capital letter | I | question mark | ? |
| full stop | . | speech marks | " " |

20

b

_____

_____

_____

_____

Check

capital letters D + W   question mark   ?

full stop   •   speech marks   " "

Activity 6
Build a sentence

disgusting _____

_____

_____

_____

_____

Activity 7
Edit

Find 6 errors.

I'm afraid not! hooted sam.
i bought the chains for
Hallowe'en!

Check

2 capital letters   speech marks   " "   " "

21

Activity 9
Composition

Write a poem about what you can buy at Wailing Winny's car boot sale.

The car boot sale

_____

_____

_____

_____

_____

_____

_____

_____

_____

Power words
useless foul horrible vile mouldy

22

Toad

**Activities
1, 2, 3, 4**
Spelling

Green words

voi ce   hope   home   throat   coat

Red words

w(ou)ld   th(ere)   c(o)me   (a)ny(o)ne   w(a)ter

Your words

Activity 5
Hold a
sentence

ⓐ

_____

_____

_____

_____

_____

Check
capital letters P+J   full stop .

23

b
_____
_____
_____
_____

Check

capital letters T + K   full stop .

Activity 6
Build a sentence

deceitful _____
_____
_____
_____

Activity 7
Edit

Find 6 errors.

What's wrong, Princess Joan croaked the toad. You woke me up, with your moaning and groaning

Check

question mark ?   speech marks " " " "
exclamation mark !

Activity 9
Composition

Write notes about what the characters did and thought.

Power words

loathsome   hideous   slimy   deceitful

Write about what lessons the characters learned.

lesson learned

_____

_____

_____

_____

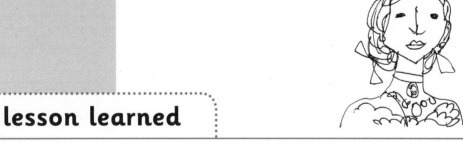

lesson learned

_____

_____

_____

_____

lesson learned

_____

_____

_____

_____

lesson learned

_____

_____

_____

_____

See *Get Writing!* Handbook for lesson plans.

Andrew

**Activities
1, 2, 3, 4**
Spelling

Green words

kn ew*   grew   drew   threw   reall`y

*Pronounce ew as 'oo'

Red words

where   could   what   here   someone

Your words

Activity 5
Hold a
sentence

ⓐ

_____

_____

_____

_____

_____

Check
capital letters W + A   question mark   ?

(b)

_____

_____

_____

Check

capital letter   W   question mark ?

Activity 6
Build a sentence

disappeared _____

_____

_____

_____

_____

Activity 7
Edit

Find 6 errors.

then someone shouted, andrew! andrew! can you see me?

Check

4 capital letters   speech marks   " "

Activity 9
Composition

a Make notes about what happened to you when you were lost at sea.

Power words
terrified   horrified   scanned   disappeared

Activity 9
Composition

 b **Write about what happened.**

Wednesday 9 June

The first thing I remember is _____

_____

_____

The wind had blown up _____

_____

_____

The sea was _____

_____

_____

The beach disappeared _____

_____

_____

I scanned the shoreline _____

_____

_____

Dear Vampire

See *Get Writing! Handbook* for lesson plans.

**Activities
1, 2, 3, 4**
Spelling

Green words

year   hear   ear   fear   fire

Red words

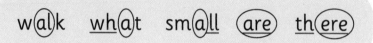

walk   what   small   are   there

Your words

Activity 5
Hold a
sentence

(a)

_____

_____

_____

_____

Check

capital letters O + W + I   full stop .

exclamation marks   ! + !

speech marks   " " " "

b

_____

_____

_____

Check

capital letters I + W speech marks " "

full stop • apostrophe '

exclamation mark !

Activity 6
Build a
sentence

terrifying _____

_____

_____

Activity 7
Edit

Find 6 errors.

sam was dancing with nelly
dave was playing a tune on
his dustbin lids. phil was
lighting the fireworks

Check

4 capital letters full stops ..

Activity 9
Composition

Power words
terrifying
horrifying
frightening
blood-curdling

(a) **Make notes for your writing.**

b **Write a letter to the vampire. Give him some good advice about how to be more scary.**

Dear Aunt Horrible,

I am sad and confused. I was asked to terrify a group of witches and ghouls but it all went wrong. They said I was the worst vampire ever. I came as a bat, which I thought was pretty frightening but they just thought I was pathetic and really a rather rubbish vampire. Help me, please...

Dear Vampire, _____

_____

_____

_____

_____

_____

_____

_____

_____

_____

_____

Vulture culture

**Activities
1, 2, 3, 4**
Spelling

Green words

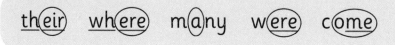

huge   white   year   more   be`cause

Red words

their   where   many   were   come

Your words

Activity 5 ⓐ
Hold a
sentence

Check

capital letter   W   question mark   ?

(b)

_____

_____

_____

Check

capital letter   W   question mark ?

Activity 6
Build a
sentence

scavenge/scavenger   _____

_____

_____

Activity 7
Edit

Find 6 errors.

there are now many more
condors the future looks good
for these proud creatures we
will have the pleasure of seeing
them for many years to come

Check

3 capital letters   full stops   •••

Activity 9
Composition

a **Write notes about the Marabou stork.**

Power words
cloak-like
scavenger
capture
colony

The Marabou stork from Africa is also known as the 'undertaker bird' because of its huge, black, cloak-like wings. It has skinny white legs and a pink bald head and it stands 150 cm tall. It has the same wingspan as the Andean condor which, at 3.5 m, is the largest of any bird.

Like the Andean condor, the Marabou stork is a scavenger, eating dead animals. It can also capture small animals and birds such as rats and doves. It lays up to 3 eggs at a time and nests on cliff edges or in trees in a colony with other Marabou storks.

- Looks like: _____

_____

- Eats: _____

_____

- Lives: _____

_____

- Breeds: _____

_____

b Write about the Marabou stork and the Andean condor.

Similarities and differences between the Marabou stork and the Andean condor

A celebration on planet Zox

**Activities
1, 2, 3, 4**
Spelling

Green words

sta`tion   sec`tion   trad`i`tion   expl<u>ore</u>
inv<u>ite</u>

Red words

w(or)<u>se</u>   c(a)ll   s(ai)d   <u>sh</u>(ou)<u>l</u>d   w(a)<u>tch</u>

Your words

Activity 5
Hold a
sentence

ⓐ

_____

_____

_____

_____

Check
capital letters   M+M   full stop   .

(b)

_____

_____

_____

Check

capital letters W + C   speech marks " "

full stop   .   apostrophe '

question mark   ?

Activity 6
Build a sentence

dizzy _____

_____

_____

Activity 7
Edit

Find 6 errors.

Cosmic Clive climbed out of the tail section of the spacecraft. his face was pale green with exhaustion welcome back, Cosmic Clive! the King of Zox said

Check

2 capital letters   speech marks   " "

full stops   ..

Activity 9
Composition

a **Write notes about how Clive feels.**

Power words
light-headed
burning up
sweaty
aching all
over

_____

_____

_____

_____

_____

_____

_____

_____

_____

_____

_____

How did you feel
before you fell over?

_____

_____

_____

Can I look at your
tummy? What do the
spots feel like, and when
did they appear?

_____

_____

_____

_____

Open your mouth and show me your tongue. How does your throat feel?

Wiggle your toes. Any problems there?

44

A very dangerous dinosaur

Green words

se`ri`<u>ous</u>   cu`ri`<u>ous</u>   de`li`<u>ci</u><u>ous</u>   fe`ro`<u>ci</u><u>ous</u>
pre`<u>ci</u><u>ous</u>

Red words

th<u>ough</u>t   th<u>ere</u>   wh<u>ere</u>   thr<u>ough</u>   w<u>oul</u>d

Your words

(a)

_____

_____

_____

Scrumptious!

Check

capital letters   H+S   exclamation mark   !
full stops   . .   speech marks   " "

b

_____

_____

_____

Check

capital letter   I   comma   ,

    full stop   .   speech marks   " "

Activity 6
Build a sentence

ferocious _____

_____

_____

Activity 7
Edit

Find 6 errors.

When she returned the two egs had gone she saw Snatchosaurus disappearing behind a rock, spitting out bits of shell "oh no," she wailed

Check

2 capital letters   1 spell   ✗

    full stops   . . .

Activity 9
Composition

a **Design and describe your dinosaur.**

_____

_____

_____

_____

_____

Power words
ferocious
devious
dangerous
deadly

b **Write a poem about Catchasnatchosaurus.**

_____

_____

_____

_____

_____

_____

_____

_____

See *Get Writing! Handbook* for lesson plans.

Activities 1, 2, 3, 4

Spelling

Note: do not use Fred fingers to spell these words.
Note: most 'ible' words do not have a root.

The invisible clothes

Green words

ho`rri`ble   po`ssi`ble   te`rri`ble   in`cre`di`ble   in`vi`si`ble

Red words

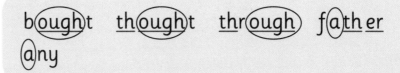

bought   thought   through   father   any

Your words

Activity 5

Hold a sentence

(a)

_____

_____

_____

Check

capital letter   I   full stop   .

speech marks   " "   apostrophe   '

exclamation mark   !

48

(b)

_____

_____

_____

Check

capital letter   I   apostrophe   '

question mark   ?

Activity 6

Build a sentence

humiliated _____

_____

_____

Activity 7

Edit

Find 6 errors.

a small boy was in the crowd with his father the Emperor isn't wearing any clothes! he whispered

Check

2 capital letters   full stops   . .

speech marks   " "

Activity 9
Composition

a **Make notes about the Emperor before and after he is tricked.**

Power words
proud
humiliated
embarrassed

Before

- <u>Feels:</u> _____
- _____
- _____
- _____

- <u>Moves:</u> _____
- _____
- _____
- _____

- <u>Thinks:</u> _____
- _____
- _____
- _____

After

- Feels: _____
- _____
- _____
- _____

- Moves: _____
- _____
- _____
- _____

- Thinks: _____
- _____
- _____
- _____

Write a letter to a friend about the trick.

A job for Jordan

**Activities
1, 2, 3, 4**
Spelling

Green words

<u>f</u>or <u>m</u>ore <u>p</u>a<u>w</u> <u>m</u>orn`i<u>ng</u>  be`<u>f</u>ore

Red words

(a)ll c(o)me th(ey) (wh)(o) y(ou)

Your words

Activity 5
Hold a
sentence

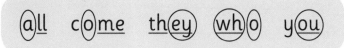

Check

capital letter H   full stop .

(b)

_____

_____

_____

Check
capital letter   D   question mark ?

Activity 6
Build a
sentence

persuade   _____

_____

_____

_____

_____

Activity 7
Edit

Find 6 errors.

all pups can be plyful, but a
guide dog pup has to behave his
owner's lif will be in his hands

Check
2 capital letters   2 spell ✗
    full stops   . .

54

Activity 9
Composition

Design a poster to raise money to train a guide dog.

Power words
support   important

A place in space: the Moon

Activities 1, 2, 3, 4
Spelling

Green words

place   take   same   shape   life

Red words

any   does   there   what   who

Your words

Activity 5
Hold a sentence

(a)

_____

_____

_____

_____

Check
capital letters T + M   full stop .

(b)

_____

_____

_____

Check

capital letters I+M   question mark   ?

Activity 6
Build a sentence

gravity _____

_____

_____

_____

Activity 7
Edit

Find 6 errors.

there is no air on the Moon if
you go to the Moon you must
tak air wiv you in tanks

Check

2 capital letters   2 spell   ✗

full stops   ••

Activity 9
Composition

(a) **Plan your poem about walking on the Moon.**

Power words
gravity
bounce
glide

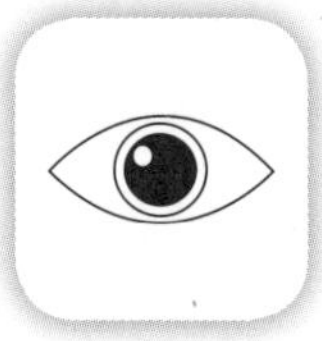

b Write your poem about walking on the Moon.

_____

_____

_____

_____

_____

_____

_____

_____

_____

Complex Speed Sounds

Consonant sounds

f	l	m	n	r	s	v	z	sh	th	ng
ff	ll	mm	nn	rr	ss	ve	zz	ti		nk
ph	le	mb	kn	wr	se		s	ci		
					c		se			
					ce					

b	c	d	g	h	j	p	qu	t	w	x	y	ch
bb	k	dd	gg		g	pp		tt	wh			tch
	ck				ge							
	ch				dge							

Vowel sounds

a	e	i	o	u	ay	ee	igh	ow
	ea				a-e	y	i-e	o-e
					ai	ea	ie	oa
						e	i	o
							y	

oo	oo	ar	or	air	ir	ou	oy	ire	ear	ure
u-e			oor	are	ur	ow	oi			
ue			ore		er					
ew			aw							
			au							

Red words to spell

I   the   said   does   do

me   he   be   she   why

no   go   so   put   what

was   were   want   of   you

your   my   to   are   her

all   small   buy   by

some   they   one

there   their   here   should

ss

Street, Oxford, OX2 6DP, United Kingdom

rsity Press is a department of the University of Oxford.
the University's objective of excellence in research, scholarship,
ation by publishing worldwide. Oxford is a registered trade mark
rd University Press in the UK and in certain other countries

Oxford University Press 2011

The moral rights of the authors have been asserted

Database right Oxford University Press (maker)

All rights reserved. No part of this publication may be reproduced, stored in a retrieval system, or transmitted, in any form or by any means, without the prior permission in writing of Oxford University Press, or as expressly permitted by law, by licence or under terms agreed with the appropriate reprographics rights organization. Enquiries concerning reproduction outside the scope of the above should be sent to the Rights Department, Oxford University Press, at the address above.

You must not circulate this book in any other binding or cover and you must impose this same condition on any acquirer.

British Library Cataloguing in Publication Data

Data available

ISBN: 978-0-19-847909-3

10 9 8 7 6

Printed in China by Hing Yip

Acknowledgements

The publisher would like to thank the following for permission to reproduce photographs: **P39a-b** rusm/iStock.com; **P53** Altrendo Images/Getty; **P54** Yuri Arcurs/Shutterstock.com; **P55** Kevin Wheatley/Shutterstock.com; **P56** Manfred Konrad/iStock.com; **P57** Media Union/Shutterstock.com; **P59** Triff/Shutterstock.com

Illustrations by Tim Archbold and Rosie Brooks

Design by PDQ

Paper used in the production of this book is a natural, recyclable product made from wood grown in sustainable forests. The manufacturing process conforms to the environmental regulations of the country of origin.

Written by Charlotte Raby
and Ruth Miskin

TEACHERS
For inspirational support plus free resources and eBooks
www.oxfordprimary.co.uk

PARENTS:
Help your child's reading with essential tips, phonics support and free eBooks
www.oxfordowl.co.uk

Hold a sentence texts

Storybook 1: Rex to the rescue

a) What was the big problem between the dogs?

b) "Sploosh!" barked Duke, with his mouth full of green slime.

Storybook 2: The lion's paw

a) "You have broken the law," he said.

b) "You must be punished," he shouted.

Storybook 3: I dare you

a) What is Rob's first dare to Clare?

b) Why does he think Clare's dare is not fair?

Storybook 4: Looking after a hamster

a) What do you need to buy for your hamster?

b) What can you make hamster toys from?

Storybook 5: How silly!

a) "The sun has fallen into the pond!" he shouted.

b) "Why have you done such a silly thing?" she asked.

Storybook 6: Wailing Winny's car boot sale

a) "Is it dustbin day?" he grunted.

b) "Did you buy a pair of trainers at the sale?" wailed Winnie.

Storybook 7: Toad

a) Princess Joan lived in a palace by a lake.

b) The King often boasted about her good looks.

Storybook 8: Andrew

a) Why was Andrew really scared?

b) What if he floated here forever?

Storybook 9: Dear Vampire

a) "Oh dear!" wailed Winnie. "I wanted a scary vampire!"

b) "I'm getting tired of this!" wailed Winny.

Storybook 10: Vulture culture

a) Why do you think condors should be protected?

b) Why do they stay with their parents for so long?

Storybook 11: A celebration on planet Zox

a) Mum was deep in conversation with Meg.

b) "Will he need an operation?" asked Clare's mum.

Storybook 12: A very dangerous dinosaur

a) He wiped his hideous mouth. "Scrumptious!" he cried.

b) "It is a very dangerous dinosaur," he said.

Storybook 13: The invisible clothes

a) "I can't see the cloth!" he cried miserably.

b) Isn't this the most remarkable fabric you have ever seen?

Non-fiction Book 1: A job for Jordan

a) He is trained in some more important lessons.

b) Do you want to sponsor a guide dog pup?

Non-fiction Book 5: A place in space: the Moon

a) The Moon is the same shape as a ball.

b) Is the Moon high up in space?

Get Writing! Grey Book 7

The **Get Writing! Books** contain a wide range of writing activities which are linked to the Storybooks and Non-fiction Books to make the strong link between reading and writing. Lesson plans for the writing activities are provided in the **Get Writing! Handbook**.

The writing activities and features include:

- Remembering and writing a sentence

- Finding spelling and punctuation errors in a sentence

- Composition activities which develop children's writing step-by-step from simple sentences to extended texts. Children write a variety of texts including: dialogue, recounts, non-chronological reports, instructions, descriptive texts, writing from experience, labels, poems and letters

- 'Check' boxes which prompt children to review their writing throughout

- Focus on 'power words' which encourages children to use ambitious vocabulary in their writing.

Use the **Get Writing! Books** with the Storybooks as follows:

Get Writing! Red Ditty Books 1–10	Red Ditty Books 1–10
Get Writing! Green B...	...en Storybooks 1–10
Get Writing! Pur...	...le Storybooks 1–10
Get Writing! Pink...	...Storybooks 1–10
Get Writing! Oran...	...nge Storybooks 1–12
Get Writing! Yello...	Set 5 Yellow Storybooks 1–10
Get Writing! Blue Book 6	Set 6 Blue Storybooks 1–10
Get Writing! Grey Book 7	Set 7 Grey Storybooks 1–13

9780198478942

Not to be photocopied

OXFORD
UNIVERSITY PRESS

How to get in touch:
web   www.oxfordprimary.co.uk
email schools.enquiries.uk@oup.com
tel.   +44 (0) 1536 452610
fax   +44 (0) 1865 313472

Read Write Inc. Phonics
Get Writing! Grey Book 7 Pack of 10:
978-0-19-847908-6
Get Writing! Mixed Pack of 17:
978-0-19-847894-2